Blue Sky
STUDIOS

SNOOPY AND CHARLiE BROWN
THE PEANUTS MOViE
by Schulz

Based on the Peanuts comic strip created by Charles M Schulz

Adapted by Fiona Davis from the original screenplay by
Craig Schulz, Bryan Schulz and Cornelius Uliano

Popcorn
ELT
Readers

Meet ...
everyone from

Charlie Brown

This is Charlie Brown.
This is his dog, Snoopy.

Snoopy

Sally

Sally is Charlie
Brown's sister.

At Charlie Brown's school this year there is

a talent show   and a school dance.

This is Charlie Brown's kite.

Peppermint Patty

Lucy

Linus

These are Charlie Brown's friends.

And there is a new girl ...

The little red-haired girl

Before you read ...
What do you think?
Does Charlie Brown like the little red-haired girl?

New Words

What do these new words mean? Ask your teacher or use your dictionary.

cow / cowgirl

The **cowgirl** has a lot of **cows**.

baseball

He loves **baseball**.

fire sprinkler

This is a **fire sprinkler**.

cheer

The boys and girls are **cheering**.

help

He is **helping** his mum.

kick

She is **kicking** the ball.

talent show

It is a **talent show**.

magic trick

Wow! It's a **magic trick**.

test

They are doing a **test** at school today.

pretty

She is **pretty**.

'Never give up!'

Never give up!

THE PEANUTS MOViE

CHAPTER ONE
'Who is the little red-haired girl?'

'Today is a good day,' says Charlie Brown. 'It's sunny. It's windy. And I've got a new kite.'

Charlie Brown runs with his kite.

But there is a lot of wind.
'Aaaaah!' shouts Charlie Brown.

Suddenly, the wind stops. The kite stops too.
'Oh no!' says Charlie Brown.

There is a new girl in town. She has red hair.

'Who is the little red-haired girl?' says
Charlie Brown.

'Does she like baseball?' asks Peppermint
Patty.

'Is she pretty?' asks Lucy.

The little red-haired girl is at school.

'She likes writing!' says Peppermint Patty.
'She *is* very pretty,' says Lucy.
Charlie Brown says nothing. He likes the
little red-haired girl.

Today there is a big test at school.
'Start writing now!' says the teacher.

Charlie Brown is thinking about the little
red-haired girl.

'Stop writing now!' says the teacher.

'Stop?' says Charlie Brown.

'Now?' asks Peppermint Patty.

Charlie Brown gives his test to the teacher. Peppermint Patty gives her test to the teacher.

'Write your names on your tests!' says the teacher. 'Quickly!'

'I don't like tests,' says Charlie Brown.

CHAPTER TWO
The talent show and the school dance

Charlie Brown wants to be friends with the little red-haired girl. Snoopy wants to help.

The little red-haired girl opens the door.

'Hello?' she says.

But Charlie Brown is not there!

The little red-haired girl wants to go to the talent show.

'What can I do in the talent show?' thinks Charlie Brown.

Charlie Brown never gives up. He does magic tricks at home with Snoopy. He does magic tricks all day and all night.

'Now I can go,' he says.

It is the night of the talent show. Charlie Brown sees his sister. She is sad.

'I want to be a cowgirl,' says Sally. 'But I don't have a cow!'

'I can help Sally!' says Charlie Brown. 'Where's Snoopy?'

Snoopy and Charlie Brown
help Sally in the talent show.
'Look!' laughs everyone.
'Charlie Brown is the cow!'
'Why me?' says Charlie Brown.

The little red-haired girl wants to go to the school dance. Charlie Brown wants to go too.

'But I can't dance,' he says.

Snoopy is a good teacher. Charlie Brown never gives up. He dances all day and all night.

'Now I can go,' he says.

It is the night of the school dance. The little red-haired girl is a good dancer.

Charlie Brown is a good dancer too. He is funny!

His friends cheer. 'Go, Charlie Brown!' they shout.

Charlie Brown can't stop dancing! He does a very good kick ... and he kicks the fire sprinkler!

'Oh no!' shouts everyone. They run home.

'Why me?' says Charlie Brown.

CHAPTER THREE
A big day for Charlie Brown

It is a big day at school.

'One boy has 100% in the test!' says the teacher.

'Who has 100%?' asks Linus.

'And it is … Charlie Brown!' says the teacher.

Everyone cheers.

'Charlie Brown is my friend!' says Linus.

Charlie Brown stands in front of everyone.
'This is a good day for Charlie Brown!' he
says.

Then Charlie Brown sees the test.

'Oh no! Why me?' he says. 'This isn't my test. It's Peppermint Patty's test.'

Charlie Brown is very sad. But then the little red-haired girl speaks to him.

'Charlie Brown,' she says. 'You can dance and you are funny! You help your sister. And you NEVER give up! I want to be your friend!'

It is good to be Charlie Brown!

THE END

Minnesota – Charlie Brown's home!

Charlie Brown and his friends are from Minnesota. Come and see Charlie Brown's home!

Where is Minnesota?

Minnesota is on the Mississippi river in the USA. The Mississippi is a very long river. It starts in Minnesota.

CANADA Minnesota

USA

The Mississippi river

Winter in Minnesota

Winter in Minnesota is very cold. Sometimes it is -11°C. There are a lot of lakes in Minnesota. In the winter there is ice on the lakes.

Charlie Brown loves his kite. Children in Minnesota love kites too.

Summer in Minnesota

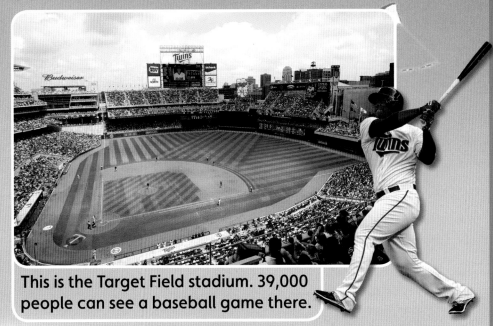

This is the Target Field stadium. 39,000 people can see a baseball game there.

Peppermint Patty loves baseball. Children in Minnesota love baseball too. In the summer you can play baseball or you can see a game.

★ What do you like doing in the winter or in the summer? ★

What do these words mean? Find out.

winter lake ice

summer people

After you read

1 Match the names and sentences.

a) Lucy

b) Charlie Brown

c) Snoopy

d) The little red-haired girl

e) Peppermint Patty

f) Sally

i) She wants to be a cowgirl.

ii) She likes writing.

iii) He never gives up.

iv) She loves baseball.

v) She has dark hair.

vi) He is a good teacher.

2 Answer the questions about the little red-haired girl. Write *Yes, she is.* or *No, she isn't.*

a) Is she a good dancer? ...Yes, she is...

b) Is she Sally's sister? ....

c) Is she Charlie Brown's friend? ....

d) Is she a cowgirl? ....

e) Is she pretty? ....

Where's the popcorn?
Look in your book.
Can you find it?

Puzzle time!

1 Complete the sentences about Charlie Brown.

a) He is h <u>e l p</u> ing Sally.

b) He is t _ _ _ _ ing about the little red-haired girl.

c) He is s _ _ _ _ ing in front of everyone.

d) He is doing a m _ _ _ _ t _ _ _ _ .

e) He is d _ _ _ ing.

f) He is doing a t _ _ _ .

2 Look at the pictures in exercise 1 again. Colour the stars.

a) My favourite picture =

b) My favourite part of the story =

c) Charlie Brown's favourite part of the story =

3 Answer the questions.

a, b, c ... x, y, z = letters
a, e, i, o, u = vowels

a) PEANUTS How many vowels are in this word?

2 ③ 4

b) Charlie How many letters are in this name?
Brown 7 10 12

c) Charlie How many vowels are in this name?
Brown 3 4 5

d) Write the vowels in these names.

i) S n _ _ p y   ii) L _ c y

iii) P _ p p _ r m _ n t P _ t t y

4 Draw your favourite character. Then complete the sentences about the character.

My favourite character is

....

He / She has ....

....

He / She likes ....

....

Imagine ...

1 Work with two friends. Act out the scenes.

A

Charlie Brown	Who is the little red-haired girl?
Peppermint Patty	Does she like baseball?
Lucy	Is she pretty?

B

| **Peppermint Patty** | She likes writing! |
| **Lucy** | She *is* very pretty. |

2 Imagine a new boy or girl is at your school. What do you say? Write a new dialogue. Act it out for your friends.

Chant

1  Listen and read.

Charlie Brown

He can dance all day,
He can dance all night.
He does magic tricks
And he runs with a kite!

2 Say the chant.